STAR WARS™

Jedi Adventures

LONDON, NEW YORK, MUNICH,
MELBOURNE, AND DELHI

Editorial Lead Heather Jones
Senior Production Editor Clare McLean
Production Editor Kavita Varma
Managing Editor Catherine Saunders
Managing Art Editor Ron Stobbart
Brand Manager Lisa Lanzarini
Publishing Manager Simon Beecroft
Category Publisher Alex Allan
Production Controller Katherine Whyte

Lucasfilm
Executive Editor Jonathan W. Rinzler
Art Director Troy Alders
Keeper of the Holocron Leland Chee
Director of Publishing Carol Roeder
Reading Consultant Linda B. Gambrell, Ph.D.

This edition published in Canada in 2010
Dorling Kindersley is represented in Canada by
Tourmaline Editions Inc
662 King Street West
Suite 304 Toronto, Ontario M5V 1M7

First published in the United States in 2005–2010 as
four separate titles: *Star Wars: Join the Rebels 2010, Star
Wars: I Want to be a Jedi 2007, Star Wars: Star Pilot 2005,
Star Wars: The Story of Darth Vader 2008*
004-180394-Oct/10

A catalog record for this book is available from the
Library of Congress.

ISBN: 978-1-55363-152-1

Color reproduction by Media Development Printing Ltd,
UK. Printed and bound in China by
L Rex Printing Co., Ltd.

**Discover more at
www.dk.com**

www.starwars.com

STAR WARS
Jedi Adventures

Contents

STAR WARS
Join the Rebels

Written by Catherine Saunders

My name is Luke Skywalker.
I live on Tatooine with my
Uncle Owen and Aunt Beru.

My uncle wants me to be a farmer but I would prefer to go to the Imperial Academy.

I want to be a pilot like my friend Biggs Darklighter.

C-3PO and R2-D2

Uncle Owen bought these droids from Jawa traders. C-3PO is a protocol droid. He can speak many languages. R2-D2 is an astromech droid.

My life is very quiet on Tatooine.
It is a remote desert planet.
Every day, I help my uncle on
his moisture farm.
But I dream of adventure!

Life is much more exciting in
other parts of the galaxy.
It is also more dangerous.
An evil Emperor rules the
galaxy. He has built
a powerful weapon
that can destroy
a whole planet.
It is called the
Death Star.

Some brave people have joined together to try and defeat the Emperor. They are called the Rebel Alliance. I would like to join them. The Emperor wants to destroy the Rebels but he does not know where to find them.

The Rebels have a secret base on Yavin 4. This is where they plan secret attacks on the Empire.

This is Leia. She is a Princess and one of the Rebel leaders. She has been on many daring missions for the Rebels but now she is being held captive by the evil Sith Lord Darth Vader.

My uncle's new droid R2-D2 has
a message from Princess Leia.
She needs help from Jedi Master
Obi-Wan Kenobi.
 I am going to help, too!

Darth Vader

Darth Vader was once
a famous Jedi but now
he serves the Emperor.
He wants to crush the
Rebel Alliance.

Princess Leia has hidden the blueprints of the Death Star inside R2-D2. Obi-Wan and I must take them to Princess Leia's home planet, Alderaan. We need to go there quickly! The *Millennium Falcon* will fly us there. It is one of the fastest ships in the galaxy.

Han Solo is its captain and a Wookiee named Chewbacca is his first mate.

The planet Alderaan has been
destroyed by the Death Star!
Now we are caught in a tractor
beam and are being pulled toward
the Death Star.

I am a long way from Tatooine and heading straight into a thrilling adventure.
I am determined to rescue Princess Leia and join the Rebel Alliance.

Being a Rebel hero is not easy.
The Imperial stormtroopers are
firing at us from all directions.
Now we are trapped in a smelly
garbage dump.

After many adventures, we escape from the Death Star and rejoin the Rebel Alliance. I am ready to help the Rebels fight back against the evil Empire.

Rebel pilots must be ready for action at all times. We are on a mission to destroy the Death Star. It is very dangerous but I am learning to use the Force.

The Force
The energy that surrounds all living things.
Jedi knights use the power of the Force. Sith
lords use the dark side of the force for evil.

I am flying a ship called an
X-wing and the Imperial pilots are
attacking us in TIE fighters.
Many of my brave Rebel friends
have already been lost. Luckily I
have scored a direct hit and the
Death Star is destroyed.

My first mission was a success.
The Rebels were triumphant
and everyone was so happy.
I felt like a hero.
Now I am learning that being a
Rebel is hard work. Imperial spies
are everywhere and we must
always be on the look out
for them.

The new Rebel base on Hoth is very cold.

The Imperial forces have discovered our new base! The stormtroopers have giant AT-AT walkers and are trying to destroy our power source.

The Rebels are ready for action and are not going to give up without a fight. I have a plan…
This battle is over and the Rebels must flee from Hoth.
We will live to fight another day.

The Battle of Hoth was a victory for the Empire but the Rebels are not beaten yet. We will overcome the Empire and free the galaxy. I am going to Dagobah to meet the famous Yoda and learn the ways of the Force. I will become a great Jedi warrior.

Yoda
Yoda may be small but he is a very powerful and wise Jedi. He senses that Luke has great powers and shows him how to use them.

The Force is showing me that
my good friends Han Solo and
Princess Leia are in danger.

Darth Vader has set a trap for them in Cloud City.

I need to rescue them.

I was right. Darth Vader is here.

I must fight him and help free my friends.

The Rebel Alliance is growing stronger. There is a new Death Star. We have a plan to destroy it and finally defeat the Empire.

Moon of Endor
Endor's forest moon is home to creatures called Ewoks. They may look cute but they are tough! The Ewoks help the Rebels to destroy the new Death Star.

The Death Star's shield generator is located on the moon of Endor. The Rebels are going to attack it!

The plan is working.
The shield generator is destroyed
and the Rebel pilots are attacking
the Imperial fleet.

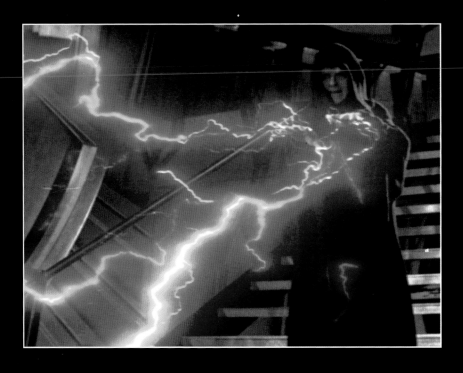

It is time for me to face the
Emperor himself. The Emperor is
very powerful. But at the last
moment, Darth Vader turns away
from the dark side and defeats the
Emperor. The Rebels have won
and the galaxy is free at last.

Glossary

Blueprints
Plans showing a map of where everything is on board.

Daring
Brave and adventurous.

the Force
The special power that both Jedi and Sith can learn to use.

Imperial Academy
This is where the Galactic Empire trains its army.

Jawa
The people who live on Tatooine.

Remote
A long way from anywhere else.

Shield generator
The machine that makes the protective shield around the
Death Star.

Sith Lord
A high-ranking member of the Sith race.

Tractor Beam
A beam that can trace other ships and pull them in.

Triumphant
Happy, victorious, jubilant. Usually when you have won
something, you would feel triumphant.

Wookiee
A hairy being that lives on the planet Kashyyyk.

STAR WARS
I WANT TO BE A
JEDI

Written by Simon Beecroft

Mace Windu

Obi-Wan Kenobi

The Jedi

If you want to be a Jedi, you must learn all about Jedi ways. You must train hard. The Jedi are the best fighters in the galaxy, but their job is to keep the peace. A Jedi trains hard for many years. Then he or she travels around the galaxy to wherever there is trouble. The Jedi do all they can to bring peace without using violence.

A Jedi learns about a powerful energy field called the Force. The Force is everywhere. A Jedi must be able to understand and use the Force.

Yoda

Great Power
The Force is a special energy. You cannot see it, but you can learn to feel it. Yoda, a Jedi, uses the Force to help others in the galaxy.

Jedi usually go on missions in pairs.

Long Training

To be a Jedi, you must start your training when you are very young. First you will be a Youngling. If you pass the tests, you become a Padawan Learner. This means you are training to be a Jedi, but you are not a Jedi yet. If you train hard for several years and pass more tests, you will become a Jedi Knight.

When you are a Padawan you will go on missions, but never alone. A more experienced Jedi will always go with you. A Jedi Master is the most experienced Jedi of all. One day, if you continue to learn and train, you too could become a Jedi Master. Then you will train other, younger Jedi apprentices. This is how the Jedi Order works.

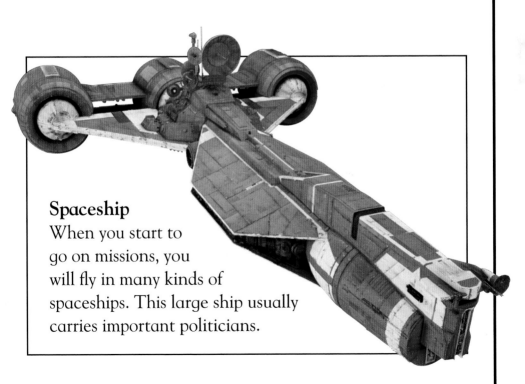

Spaceship
When you start to go on missions, you will fly in many kinds of spaceships. This large ship usually carries important politicians.

Special Powers

Jedi can come from anywhere in the galaxy. When they are very young, a boy or girl discovers that they have a special power. Perhaps they can move objects with their mind or they can do something really fast. They are using the Force without realizing it. This means that they could be a good Jedi.

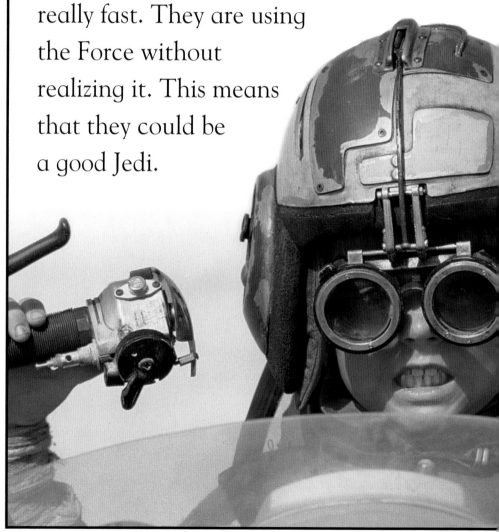

One such person was Anakin Skywalker. Although he was very young, he was a great pilot. He flew a very fast machine called a Podracer and won a very dangerous race. A Jedi Master called Qui-Gon Jinn (pronounced KWY-GONN-JIN) met Anakin and decided to train him to be a Jedi. Qui-Gon Jinn thought that Anakin could become a great Jedi.

Anakin Skywalker is determined to win the Podrace.

Jedi in Training

When you begin training to be a Jedi you must leave your home and your parents. It's hard to leave behind everyone you love, so you must really want to be a Jedi. You travel from your home to a big planet at the center of the galaxy. A building called the Jedi Temple will be your home for the rest of your life. Here is where your Jedi training begins.

A New Home
The Jedi Temple is a gigantic building where all Jedi live, train, and work. It contains training halls, meeting rooms, libraries, and huge hangars for spaceships.

Using a training device, Jedi Master Yoda teaches the Younglings how to "see" without using their eyes.

At the Jedi Temple, you have many classes to learn all the Jedi skills. You learn to control your emotions so that you do not feel fear, anger, or hatred. You learn to use the Force. Sometimes, you will wear a special training helmet that covers your eyes. You will to learn to "see" only by using the Force.

Master and Learner

When you are training to be a Jedi, you spend a lot of time with your teacher. Your teacher will be a Jedi Master. You will travel everywhere together. You must always be prepared to learn from your teacher.

Anakin Skywalker's teacher was called Obi-Wan Kenobi (pronounced OH-BEE-ONE KEN-OH-BEE). Anakin felt that Obi-Wan was holding him back.

Anakin does not always listen to what Obi-Wan Kenobi tells him.

Anakin believes that Chancellor Palpatine is a good man and listens to his advice.

Anakin was impatient to become a Jedi Knight. He was more powerful than most Jedi, but he did not always obey the rules of the Jedi Order. Anakin shared his feelings of frustration with Chancellor Palpatine (pronounced PAL-PA-TEEN). Anakin thought that Palpatine was a good friend to him.

Forbidden Marriage

Like everyone, the Jedi can fall in love, but they must not allow any strong emotions to get in the way of defending the galaxy. The Jedi are forbidden to marry because strong emotional attachments can cloud their judgment and stop them from doing their jobs well.

Anakin Skywalker knew that he was not allowed to get married, but he fell in love with a beautiful woman called Padmé Amidala (pronounced PAD-MAY AM-EE-DAL-AH). Anakin and Padmé secretly got married. If anyone found out that Anakin was married, he would have to stop being a Jedi.

The Jedi Council

The most powerful and wise Jedi sit on the Jedi High Council. Their job is to make all the most important decisions. Twelve Jedi sit on the Council at any one time. The Jedi Council meets in one of the tall towers of the Jedi Temple. Two of the most important members of the Jedi Council are Yoda and Mace Windu.

Yoda is a very wise, green-skinned alien who is many hundreds of years old. Mace Windu is a human Jedi with great powers of thought. Yoda and Mace are both highly skilled with the Jedi's only weapon, which is called a lightsaber.

Mace Windu

Lightsabers

Lightsabers work like swords, but the blade is not made of metal. A lightsaber blade is made of glowing energy that can be many different colors. It is much more powerful than a metal blade, so a Jedi must learn how to use it safely and carefully. This is an important part of a Jedi's training.

Qui-Gon protects Queen Amidala from a battle droid.

Jedi must never use their lightsabers to attack others. They must use them only to defend and protect. Jedi are taught to respect life in any form.

Jedi build their own lightsabers, so every lightsaber is different. If you lose your lightsaber you must build another one yourself.

Lightsaber handle
You hold your lightsaber by the handle. When you activate it, the blade comes out of the end. The blade can slice through almost anything.

Lightsaber Combat

The Jedi use their lightsabers to defend themselves and others. Lightsabers can stop objects or deflect blaster fire. They can slice open sealed doors. Sometimes a Jedi has to fight someone else with a lightsaber. The Jedi use many fast moves to block their opponent. They use the Force to make their movements faster.

They also use the Force to guess what moves their opponent will make, even before they have made them.

Jedi Master Qui-Gon fights a deadly enemy named Darth Maul.

Mind Tricks

The Jedi can use the Force to influence the actions of other people. With a special wave of the hand, a Jedi can tell a person what he or she wants them to think or do. The person repeats back what the Jedi has just said, unaware that the Jedi has put the thought in their mind. This is called a Jedi mind trick.

Jedi mind tricks only work on certain people. They do not work on everyone. Certain strong-willed people can resist the Jedi mind trick.

All in the Mind
Once Obi-Wan used a Jedi mind trick on a small-time criminal. He convinced the crook to start living an honest life.

Anakin Skywalker used to be a slave
owned by a flying alien called Watto.
Qui-Gon tried to free Anakin by using
a mind trick on Watto, but Watto could
not be influenced.

Mind Powers

Jedi can also use the Force to move objects without touching them. For a Jedi, there is no difference between a large object and a small object. A skilled Jedi can move objects of any size—large or small.

Great Teacher
Yoda taught a young Jedi called Luke Skywalker
how to lift heavy objects using the Force. At first
Luke found it hard to believe it was possible.

Wise Jedi like Yoda can lift very heavy
objects using their mind alone. Yoda can
lift heavy rocks and even raise a spaceship
out of a swamp!

Jedi mind powers are also useful if a Jedi
drops his lightsaber in a battle. He can
quickly make it jump back into his hand
using the Force.

Jedi Equipment

The Jedi carry certain special tools
when they go on a mission. They never
know what they might need! They carry
their tools on a special belt called a utility
belt. They can hang their lightsaber on
their utility belt. The belt also holds a
medical kit, tools, food capsules, and
a special communication device called
a comlink. The Jedi use comlinks to send
and receive messages.

*Qui-Gon uses his comlink to speak with
Obi-Wan Kenobi.*

Comlink

*Qui-Gon uses his holoprojector to show
realistic pictures of a spaceship.*

Another useful Jedi device is called
a holoprojector, which enables a Jedi
to record an image and

Holoprojector

then play it back later.
A holoprojector can
also transmit a
moving image of
yourself to someone
else, like a video link.

Special Missions

Special missions require special equipment. If you are going to swim underwater for long periods of time, you will need a Jedi breather. It fits into your mouth so you can breathe air through it. It holds enough air to last for two hours. Qui-Gon Jinn and Obi-Wan Kenobi once used breathers to reach an underwater city on the planet of Naboo.

Another useful device is a pair of macrobinoculars. They electronically zoom in on objects that are very far away. They even work in the dark!

Tracer Beacon

If you want to keep track of a suspect, you could stick a tracer beacon to their spaceship. It sends signals that enable you to follow the spaceship.

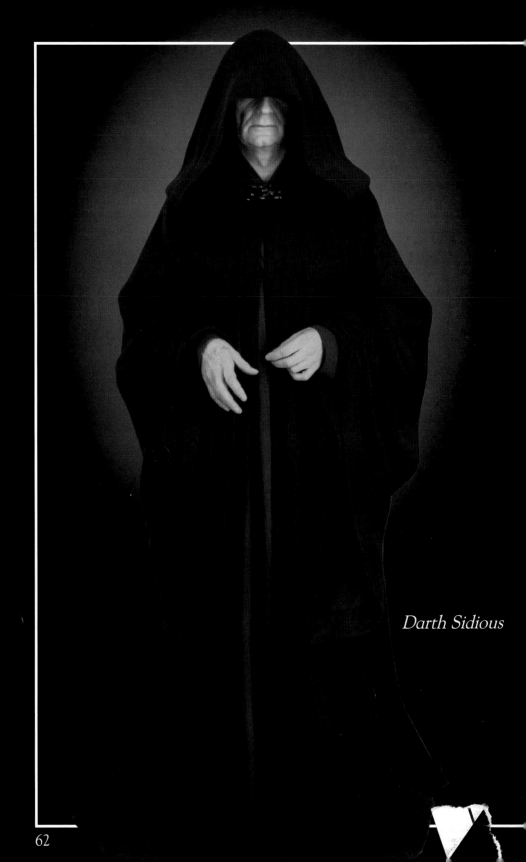

Darth Sidious

Deadly Enemies

The Jedi's deadly enemies are called the Sith. The first Sith were once Jedi, but they turned bad. Most Jedi use the Force for good but the Sith use the dark side of the Force to gain greater powers. The Sith want to destroy the Jedi.

A long time ago, the Sith and the Jedi fought a war. The Jedi defeated the Sith—or so they thought. Unknown to the Jedi, one Sith Master survived. The Sith Master secretly trained one other person so his skills would be passed on when he died. For a thousand years, each Sith Master trained one other person to keep the Sith skills alive. The final Sith Master was called Darth Sidious (pronounced SID-EE-US). He planned to destroy the Jedi once and for all.

Sith Battles

Sidious trained a ferocious alien called Maul. Maul had tattoos all over his head and horns on his skull. His teeth were razor sharp and his eyes were yellow. Maul fought with a deadly lightsaber with two blades, one at each end. He was a very fast fighter and the dark side of the Force gave him terrifying strength.

The Sith use lightsabers with red blades.

Sidious sent Maul to kill Qui-Gon and Obi-Wan. Maul killed Qui-Gon, but he was eventually defeated by Obi-Wan.

Dooku
When Maul was killed, Sidious had to find someone else to train. He found a Jedi Master called Dooku. Dooku had left the Jedi order and could not resist the chance to become a Sith.

Unusual Enemy

The Jedi and the Sith are usually
the only people who uses lightsabers.
However, the Sith Count Dooku trained
a man-droid to use a lightsaber.
His name was General Grievous
(pronounced GREE-VUS). General
Grievous fought with stolen lightsabers.
Each time he killed a Jedi in battle,
he took the Jedi's lightsaber.

Grievous was a deadly foe because his two mechanical arms could split into four. This meant he could fight with four lightsabers at the same time. During a war in the galaxy, Grievous fought Obi-Wan Kenobi. Grievous wanted to kill Obi-Wan and steal his lightsaber. The battle was ferocious, but in the end Obi-Wan managed to defeat Grievous.

War!

For thousands of years the Jedi were
peacekeepers in the galaxy. The Jedi had
no idea that the Sith were planning to
destroy them. Anakin's friend Chancellor
Palpatine was actually the Sith Lord
Sidious. Sidious created huge armies of
droids and started a war in the galaxy.

The first battle was on a dusty red
planet called Geonosis (pronounced
GEE-O-NO-SIS). The droid armies
attacked the Jedi. Massive tanks on
giant legs walked across the battlefield,
firing all the time. Many Jedi were
killed. Next, the droid armies began to
attack planets, one after another.

Jedi Knight, Aayla Secura, goes into battle on a boggy world covered in giant fungus plants.

Brave Generals

When war began, the Jedi had to stop the droid armies from attacking every planet in the galaxy. There were far fewer Jedi in the galaxy than droid armies. Many Jedi became great generals. Yoda was commander of all the armies, with Mace alongside him.

The Jedi fought battles on many
strange planets. Aayla Secura
(pronounced AY-LA SEK-URE-RAH)
went to a planet covered in dense jungles
to stop an enemy attack. Ki-Adi-Mundi
(pronounced KEE-ADDY-MUNDY) led
an army to a dangerous enemy planet
covered with crystals.

Ki-Adi-Mundi is a Jedi Master of great
power and skill.

Jedi Pilots

The Jedi are some of the best pilots in the galaxy. Often they use their Force powers when they are flying spaceships.

Anakin Skywalker is one of the best pilots in the galaxy. He can fly at top speed using his Force powers. The Jedi can fly many kinds of vehicles, including flying cars called airspeeders. Once, Obi-Wan piloted an underwater ship called a bongo!

Anakin uses all his Jedi skills to fly an airspeeder through a busy city.

Obi-Wan pilots his Jedi starfighter away from danger.

When the Jedi go on missions, they often fly small ships called starfighters. There is just enough space for the Jedi pilot and a small droid.

Pilot Droids
Pilot droids sit in spaceships with Jedi and help them to reach their destination. This droid is called R2-D2.

Space Battle

During the war in the galaxy, Jedi flew small attack ships called Interceptors. They are faster than ordinary starfighters. During a crucial space battle of the war, hundreds of spaceships fought each other. Anakin made many brave attacks in his Interceptor.

Obi-Wan flew close by Anakin in his own ship. Obi-Wan's ship was hit by enemy fire. Although he was in great danger, he managed to land his ship and get out just in time!

Anakin and Obi-Wan fly into the heart of the space battle.

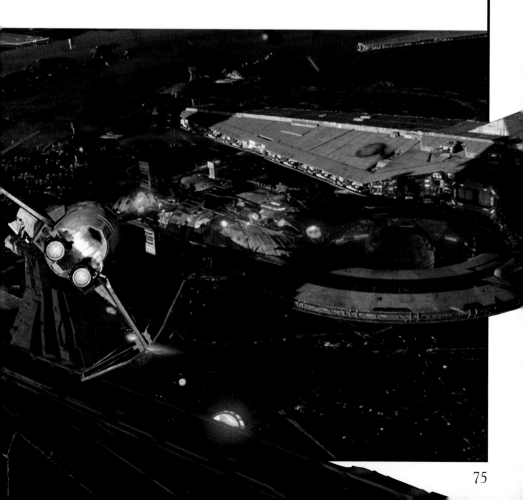

Dark Side

The worst thing a Jedi can do is to turn away from the good side of the Force and begin using the dark side. One of the most powerful Jedi of all, Anakin Skywalker, turned to the dark side during the war. The evil Sith Lord Sidious persuaded Anakin to join him and become a Sith.

Anakin turned away from his loving wife, Padmé, and attacked the Jedi Temple. He killed many Jedi. Anakin even tried to kill his oldest friend and teacher, Obi-Wan. Obi-Wan did not want to fight his old friend, but he had no choice. It took all his strength and powers, but in end he thought he had killed Anakin. He was wrong.

A New Era

The war was the most dangerous time the galaxy had ever seen. Millions of people died, including nearly all of the Jedi. The evil Sith Lords won the war and ruled the galaxy. Anakin also survived and ruled alongside Emperor Palpatine. Now he was called Darth Vader and he wore a black helmet.

Darth Vader has the body of Anakin Skywalker, but he has turned to the dark side of the Force.

Luke Skywalker never thought he would become a Jedi, but he did.

A few Jedi survived. They hid until the time was right to destroy the Sith. They were led by Anakin's children, Luke and Leia. After many long battles, the Sith were destroyed.

As long as there are Jedi, there is hope for the galaxy. May the Force be with you!

Luke Skywalker is the son of Anakin and Padmé.

Glossary

Airspeeder
A type of flying car.

Apprentice
A person who is learning a skill.

Blaster
A gun that fires a deadly beam of light.

Comlink
A communication device that sends and receives messages.

Dark side
The part of the Force associated with fear and hatred.

Droid
A kind of robot. R2-D2 is a droid.

Empire
A group of nations ruled over by one leader, who is called an Emperor. Palpatine is the Emperor who rules the Galactic Empire.

The Force
An energy field created by all living things.

Galactic
Something from or to do with a galaxy.

Galaxy
A group of millions of stars and planets.

Holoprojector
A device that records still or moving images.

Interceptors
A type of Jedi attack ship that is faster than a starfighter.

Jedi Knight
A *Star Wars* warrior with special powers who defends the good of the galaxy. Anakin Skywalker, Luke Skywalker, and Ob-Wan Kenobi are all Jedi Knights.

Jedi Master
The most experienced Jedi of all.

Jedi Order
The name of a group that defends peace and justice in the galaxy.

Jedi Temple
The Jedi headquarters where the Jedi Council meets and Jedi live, train, and work.

Lightsaber
A Jedi's and Sith's weapon, made of glowing energy.

Light side
The part of the Force associated with goodness, compassion and healing

Macrobinoculars
Binoculars that electronically zoom in on objects far away, even in the dark.

Missions
Special tasks or duties.

Padawan Learner
A Jedi who is learning the ways of the Force.

Republic
A nation or group of nations in which the people vote for their leaders.

Sith
Enemies of the Jedi who use the dark side of the Force.

Starfighter
A small, fast spaceship used by Jedi and others.

Youngling
The first stage of Jedi training, before you become a Padawan Learner.

STAR WARS
STAR PILOT

Written by Laura Buller

Into the stars

The *Star Wars* galaxy is a big place, with millions of planets in it—and it is yours to explore. But you are going to need a ride! Maybe you will take a spin in a speedy starfighter. Perhaps cruising in a silver starship is more your style. With luck, you will steer clear of the terrifying Super Star Destroyers!

In the huge *Star Wars* galaxy, you
need space vehicles for getting around.
There are thousands of different ships
zooming among the stars. Some carry
just one passenger, while others move
an entire army. This book shows you all
the important *Star Wars* spacecraft.

Welcome to the galaxy. Step in,
buckle up, and enjoy the ride!

Droid Control Ship

The Trade Federation is a powerful group of greedy merchants from all over the galaxy. Its leaders fly around in large, donut-shaped cargo ships.

The Trade Federation is unhappy with the Galactic Republic, which rules the galaxy. To prepare for war, the Trade Federation secretly changes its cargo ships into battleships. These can carry weapons and robot soldiers called battle droids.

The Droid Control Ship is the most important ship in the Trade Federation's fleet of battleships. It contains computers and special equipment that operate the battle droids by remote control. The droids will not work without signals from the Control Ship.

When a hailfire droid is after you, watch out! Each one is armed with 30 powerful weapons. These guns blast away, delivering deadly strikes as the droid races along on giant wheels.

The Trade Federation's leaders decide to show the Galactic Republic that they are powerful. So they attack the peaceful planet of Naboo.

Above Naboo, pilots control the Droid Control Ship from the ball-shaped Core Ship, which sits inside the outer ring. The Core Ship also contains the ship's reactor engine, but it is not well protected. A talented young pilot, Anakin Skywalker, discovers this for himself when he sets off a chain of explosions that destroys the entire Droid Control Ship. In Anakin's own words, "Oops!"

The Core Ship can separate from the main ship and fly about on its own.

Naboo Royal Starship

Inside and out, the Naboo Royal Starship is fit for a queen. Its engines and equipment are the very best. Inside, it is as beautiful and comfortable as any palace. Everything is neat and tidy, right down to the ship's wires and cables. The finishing touch is the ship's body. The starship is covered in shiny silver metal, a color only the queen's transport is allowed.

Because the Royal Starship travels on missions of peace, it is not armed with weapons.

The ship's body has a shiny, mirrored finish. It is polished by hand.

Padmé's starship
After she is queen, Padmé Amidala sometimes pilots this slim Royal Yacht starship herself.

During her time as elected ruler of Naboo, Queen Amidala uses the Royal Starship to make official visits. Her bodyguards, loyal handmaidens, and the ship's crew always go with her.

Podracers

Gentlemen… and scoundrels! Start your engines! Podracing is an *extremely* extreme sport popular in the *Star Wars* galaxy. Several dozen Podracers race at a time, ducking and diving through the course at speeds of more than 500 miles (800 kilometers) an hour. Pilots use every skill they have to avoid crashing.

Pilot Anakin Skywalker sits in the cockpit.

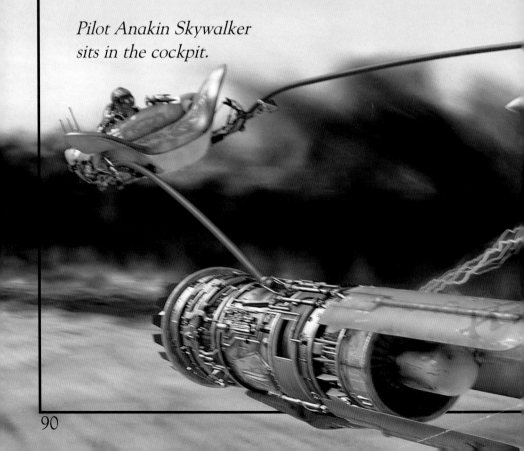

On the day of a big Podrace, you can almost taste the excitement in the air. Or is that the smell of the strong fuel that powers these super-fast vehicles?

A basic Podracer machine is made up of a cockpit, or Control Pod, where the pilot sits, attached by cables to a pair of engines. But no two Podracers are alike!

Two huge engines power the Podracer.

Podracer pilots add extra bits of machinery to their vehicles to make them faster and so shave seconds off their race times. Anakin Skywalker is the only human good enough to race. This nine-year-old boy is a skilled mechanic. He improves his Podracer, which he built himself, with spare parts he finds in the junk shop where he works.

Anakin's mechanical skills are matched by his amazing performances as a pilot. Podracing fans are still talking about his victory in the famous Boonta Eve Classic Race, in which he beat the race favorite, Sebulba.

Sebulba's tricky tactics

Anakin's main rival is alien Sebulba. He will do anything to win, including throwing bits of machinery into the engines of other Podracers.

Cables attach the pair of engines to the Control Pod.

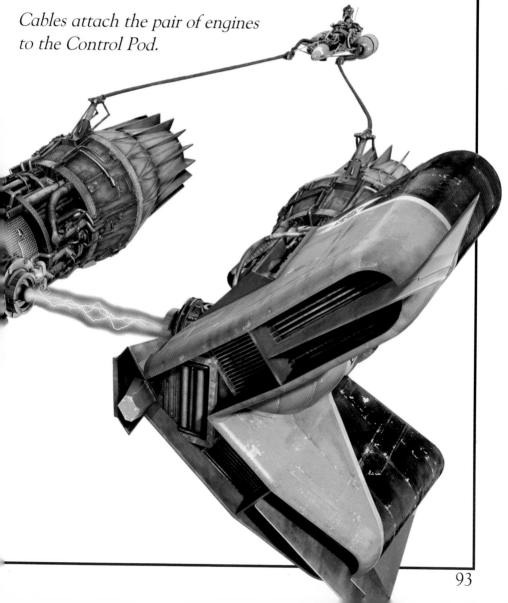

Naboo Royal N-1 starfighters

In times of peace, N-1 starfighter ships fly alongside the Queen of Naboo's Royal Starship. But if peace turns to war, they may have to use their twin blaster cannons to get out of danger!

One day, Anakin Skywalker hides in an N-1 starfighter. He accidentally turns the engines on, and the starfighter shoots into the air. It flies straight into a fierce battle between the Trade Federation and Naboo. Anakin dodges heavy fire from the enemy ships. He uses all the piloting skills he learned as a Podracer on his own planet to enter the Droid Control Ship and destroy its engines. This ends the war because the Trade Federation's army is controlled by the ship. Anakin becomes a hero.

Slave I

When Jango Fett is after you in his starship *Slave I*, there's nowhere to run and hide. Jango is a bounty hunter. Often, he captures people who are on the run from the law and collects the reward for those he finds and delivers.

A good bounty hunter needs a ship that can reach anywhere in the galaxy. The ship must have a full load of powerful weapons to use on anything in its way. It should also have a secure place to hold captives once they have been caught.

Slave I is the perfect ship for bounty hunting. Jango stole it from a prison so it already had on-board prison cells, but he made lots of improvements.

Slave I *has special
equipment that stops other
ships from seeing it coming.*

Cockpit

*Jango Fett's armored
suit and helmet
hide his identity.
He carries lots of
weapons, including
a rocket launcher.*

The main changes Jango made were to the ship's weapons. It already had blaster cannons, but he added lots of extra hidden weaponry, including laser cannons and torpedoes. He also refitted the crew quarters inside the ship to make even the longest journeys possible. The prison cells were changed to coffinlike wall cabinets to make them impossible to break out of.

Jango Fett often travels with his son, Boba. Jango pilots the ship, while Boba watches and learns from his father.

All in the family
When Boba Fett takes up his father's job, he becomes the owner of *Slave I*. He adds even more powerful weapons.

Republic gunships

When the Republic's defenders, the Jedi Knights, are surrounded by Trade Federation forces on the planet of Geonosis, the Republic gunships come to the rescue. These ships are a key part of any successful attack by the Republic. They can move army troops right into position, then take off at speed.

Each Republic gunship can transport a team of 30 soldiers and 4 speeder bikes to hot spots on the battlefield. Its thick hull resists enemy fire. It can fly through heavy cannon fire and escape with only a few dents.

The Republic gunships can also swoop down to attack ground troops and land vehicles.

Gunners fire their weapons from gun balls. There is one on either side of the ship.

Jedi starfighters

In the heat of a star battle, every second counts. Jedi Knights like Anakin Skywalker and Obi-Wan Kenobi count on their starships to help them slip through a war zone unharmed. They often fly into battle alongside larger ships like the ARC-170.

Anakin is training to be a Jedi. His starfighter is small but powerful. It started life as a standard Jedi starship, but Anakin uses his skills as a mechanic to constantly improve the vessel. He removed heavy flight instruments and bulky shields for greater speed and control. He even changed its color to yellow to remind him of his old Podracer.

Invisible Hand

The Trade Federation's flagship, *Invisible Hand*, is the most advanced starship in the fleet. Its shields and super-thick hull help to protect it from attack by enemy ships.

In one incredible battle, the leader of the Republic, Chancellor Palpatine, is captured and held prisoner on the ship.

The Republic's ARC-170 ships blast the Invisible Hand *with deadly laser fire.*

Obi-Wan Kenobi and Anakin rush to rescue the Chancellor. Inside the *Invisible Hand*, the Jedi defeat Palpatine's captors. But the ship catches fire. Even though it breaks in half, Anakin manages to land what's left of the vessel before it is destroyed by flames.

Escape pods

There are times when a quick getaway is best, especially when lives are in danger. For those times, an escape pod is a very welcome sight.

Most large starships, and even some planets, have escape pods. Smaller ships, such as starfighters, have ejector seats.

Droid friends R2-D2 and C-3PO get out of a tricky situation in this escape pod.

Yoda's lucky escape
Jedi master Yoda found himself
in a tight spot on the Wookiee
home planet of Kashyyyk.
So, he boarded this pod, pressed
the escape button, and sailed away.

These special ejector seats throw the pilot
out of a damaged ship to safety.

Escape pods are like lifeboats.
Some are only big enough for one person.
Others are designed to hold many people.
Once launched, the pods automatically
find the nearest planet to land on.

A typical escape pod has enough
supplies to keep the occupants safe
and alive until they are rescued.
Communications equipment means that
the passengers can send out calls for
help. They just have to hope that their
messages are received by someone friendly!

Imperial shuttles

The peaceful Republic has been taken over by Palpatine. He is really an evil schemer, whose only goal is power. The Republic is now Palpatine's Empire, and he has made himself Emperor.

Palpatine uses an Imperial shuttle as his personal transport. The sight of the Emperor's ship arriving like a giant bird of prey strikes fear into all who hate the Empire.

The shuttle's side wings fold down when it is in flight. They fold up when the ship is landing.

Palpatine's old ship
Even before Palpatine became
Emperor, he flew around in
his own personal shuttle.
This ship was smaller than
the later Imperial shuttle.

Important Imperial officers also
use these shuttles to get around.
One of the officers is Anakin
Skywalker, who has now become
the evil Darth Vader. Palpatine
persuaded the former Jedi
to join the vile Empire.

Each Imperial shuttle
can carry up to 20 troops,
as well as cargo. Blasting
cannons, shields,
and thick hulls protect
the ships from
enemy attack.

TIE fighters

The small ships called TIE fighters are the main starfighters of the Imperial forces. The ships are simple and cheap to build because they are made in vast numbers. TIE stands for the Twin Ion Engines that power these small ships.

TIE fighters attack one after another, sometimes hundreds at a time. A single TIE fighter may be easy to destroy, but for each one shot down, a thousand more appear.

To make these single-seater fighters
go faster, there is no heavy equipment
on the ships. The only weapons are two
laser cannons on the ball-shaped
cockpit. Often, dozens of TIE fighters
fire their cannons at the same time,
greatly increasing
their power.

Piloting a TIE fighter is a risky business. There is no life-support system on board so the pilots must wear a protective suit.

The ships are speedy and move around quickly, but they have no special shields to protect them from enemy fire. The fighters are easy targets from the side because of their large wings. It's a good thing there seems to be a steady supply of TIE pilots!

Bombs away!
Like TIE fighters, TIE bombers usually attack in groups. These bent-winged bombers are deadly. Almost every one of their ground strikes hits its target.

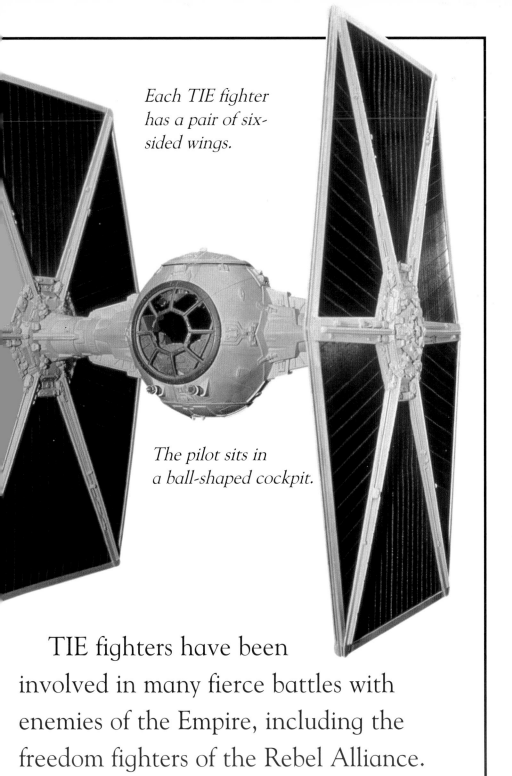

Each TIE fighter has a pair of six-sided wings.

The pilot sits in a ball-shaped cockpit.

TIE fighters have been involved in many fierce battles with enemies of the Empire, including the freedom fighters of the Rebel Alliance.

Millennium Falcon

You wouldn't know it from its battered outside, but the *Millennium Falcon* is one of the fastest vessels in the galaxy. It is owned by Han Solo, a one-time smuggler who fights with the Rebel Alliance against the Galactic Empire. The ship's copilot is the Wookiee Chewbacca.

The *Falcon* does not look like much on the surface. Its hull is beaten and battle-scarred, and the whole ship looks ready for the repair shop. But Han and Chewbacca have made many improvements to their starship over the years. It is even capable of outrunning an Imperial TIE fighter.

This is how the Millennium Falcon *gets its battle scars!*

Han and Chewbacca fly the Millennium Falcon *with C-3PO and Rebel leader, Princess Leia, on board.*

The *Millennium Falcon* is famous throughout the galaxy for breaking speed records. The saucer-shaped craft gets its super-speed from its hyperdrive engine, which Han has adjusted to make it go even faster.

The starship also carries a variety of powerful weapons, including laser cannons and missile launchers.

Secret cargo

Han built secret holds on his ship to hide smuggled goods. They come in useful when he and other Rebels have to hide there.

Han's starship has gotten him out of trouble time and time again. It may not be the best-looking vessel in the galaxy, but it never lets him down.

Han pays a visit to his starship's previous owner, Lando Calrissian. Han won the ship from Lando in a gambling game.

X-wing starfighters

An X-wing starfighter is the little ship that destroys the Empire's first Death Star, a huge super-weapon. Of course, Luke Skywalker, the brave young Rebel Alliance pilot at the controls that day, has Jedi powers to guide him. But his choice of starship definitely helps him to beat the odds.

The X-wings get their name from the shape of their wings. In battle, the wings split into an X-shape. At the end of each wing is a powerful laser cannon.

An X-wing starfighter fires on an enemy TIE fighter with its high-powered laser cannons.

The X-wings are the starfighters of the Rebel Alliance. These speedy starships are equipped with torpedo launchers and have special equipment to help guide the pilot.

The Rebel Alliance works out a plan to destroy the Death Star. If the super-weapon's engine can be hit by a torpedo, the deadly Death Star will explode.

To do this, a pilot must land a torpedo into a small hole in a deep, dark trench. The Rebel pilots are eager to have a go. Many try, but it is only future Jedi Luke Skywalker, with a little help from Han Solo in the *Millennium Falcon*, who hits the target.

After Luke blows the Death Star to bits, the X-wing starship becomes a legend among Rebel Alliance pilots. Could this be the best single-pilot starfighter ever built?

Something familiar?
Take a look at the split-wing design of the Republic's ARC-170 clonefighter ship. The X-wing starfighter is very similar to this earlier design.

Super Star Destroyer

Many things come in large sizes.
Some things come in extra-large sizes.
But the Super Star Destroyer *Executor* is
so big, it is almost off the scale! It is
the largest starship in the galaxy, at an
incredible 11.8 miles (19,000 meters) long.

This terrifying dagger-shaped giant
is evil Darth Vader's command ship.
Its enormous size is a symbol of
the strength and power of the Empire.

Darth Vader's starship is stocked with
more than 1,000 deadly weapons, ready
to use in any attack on the Rebel
Alliance. It can also carry thousands of
troops, starfighters, vehicles, and other
military equipment.

Darth Vader commands the Executor *from the bridge. The crew jump to attention when he speaks.*

The Super Star Destroyer's deflector-shield dome helps protect the ship from attack, and the communications tower makes sure the ship gets its messages across loud and clear.

The *Executor* is the first of many Super Star Destroyers to be built by the Empire to crush its enemies. But even these ships cannot stop the Rebel Alliance.

Republic assault ship
This massive transporter carries thousands of troops. The Star Destroyer and Super Star Destroyer are modeled on this earlier ship.

During one battle, an out-of-control Rebel Alliance A-wing starfighter crashes into the *Executor*'s bridge. The blast damages the Super Star Destroyer's controls. The giant ship can no longer resist the pull of the second Death Star, and the two collide in a spectacular explosion.

This pilot has lost control of his A-wing starfighter. It is spinning on a deadly collision course toward the Executor.

Glossary

Bridge
An area at the front of a large spaceship from which the ship is controlled.

Cargo
The load of goods carried by a ship.

Defender
Someone who tries to keep someone or something safe.

Droid
A kind of robot. C-3PO is a droid.

Elected
Voted for by the people.

Empire
A group of nations ruled over by one leader, who is called an emperor. Palpatine is the Emperor who rules the Galactic Empire.

Federation
A group of countries or organizations that join together because they have the same aims.

Freedom fighter
Someone who wants to be free from the rule of someone else. The Rebel Alliance are fighting for freedom from the rule of the Empire.

Galactic
Something from or to do with a galaxy.

Galaxy
A group of millions of stars and planets.

Hyperdrive
A *Star Wars* device that makes starships travel incredibly fast.

Imperial
Something from or belonging to an empire.

Jedi Knight
A *Star Wars* warrior with special powers who defends the good of the galaxy. Anakin Skywalker, Luke Skywalker, and Obi-Wan Kenobi are Jedi Knights.

Mechanic
Someone who is good at fixing and making machines.

Merchant
Someone who buys and sells things.

Planet
A giant ball-shaped rock that goes around a star. Naboo is a planet.

Rebel Alliance
A group of people in *Star Wars* who have joined together to defeat the Empire.

Republic
A nation or group of nations ruled by a government that is voted for by the people.

Schemer
Someone who makes evil plans.

Secure
Impossible to break out of.

Smuggler
Someone who secretly brings goods in and out of a place to make money from selling them.

Trade
The buying and selling of goods.

STAR WARS
THE STORY OF
DARTH VADER

Written by Catherine Saunders

The Story of Darth Vader

Take a look at Darth Vader—if you dare! He is a very dangerous man with many terrifying powers. Darth Vader is a ruthless Sith Lord who helps rule the galaxy for the evil Emperor Palpatine.

But Darth Vader was not always the masked Sith you see now. Once he was a talented Jedi Knight named Anakin Skywalker. Read on and uncover the story of how a promising young Jedi turned to the dark side of the Force.

Emperor Palpatine
From the first moment he met Anakin Skywalker, Palpatine knew that he could be the perfect apprentice.

Young Anakin Skywalker

Anakin Skywalker grew up a slave on the desert planet Tatooine. His mother Shmi could not explain how Anakin came to be born—he had no father.

Anakin was a gentle child and he loved his mother very much. From a young age he was skilled at making and fixing mechanical things. When he was nine years old he built a droid named C-3PO to help his mother. However, Anakin was impulsive and liked to take risks.

Slave owner
Anakin and Shmi were owned by a junk dealer named Watto and had to do whatever he told them. Watto made them work very hard.

A Special Calling

When Jedi Qui-Gon Jinn and Obi-Wan Kenobi landed on Tatooine to repair their damaged ship, they met Anakin Skywalker. Qui-Gon realized the young slave had the potential to be a great Jedi.

Qui-Gon checked Anakin's blood to see if he had Force powers. He certainly did!

When Anakin offered to enter a
dangerous Podrace, Qui-Gon seized the
opportunity to win the parts he needed
for his ship and Anakin's freedom. The
Jedi was sure that Anakin's Force powers
would help him to win the race. He was
right. Freed from slavery, Anakin was
able to leave Tatooine with the Jedi, but
first he had to say goodbye to his mother.

Anakin was happy to be embarking on a new adventure, but he missed his mother very much.

A New Life Begins

After leaving Tatooine, Qui-Gon asked the Jedi Council to let Anakin become his apprentice, but it refused. The Council thought that Anakin was already too old, and some wise members also sensed danger in Anakin's future.

So, when Qui-Gon and Obi-Wan went on a special mission, Anakin went too.

Padmé Amidala
Queen Padmé Amidala of Naboo was only a few years older than Anakin and the young boy developed strong feelings for her.

Anakin and the Jedi liberated the planet Naboo from the Trade Federation invasion. When Anakin piloted a starfighter and destroyed the Trade Federation's Droid Control Ship, the Jedi Council changed its mind. Although Qui-Gon had been killed by a Sith, Obi-Wan promised to train Anakin instead.

Jedi Training

Anakin Skywalker returned to the Jedi Temple on the capital planet Coruscant to begin his training. He was taught how to use and control his incredible Force powers. Anakin was also instructed in the ways of the Jedi Knights. Jedi must be calm and not governed by emotions. They are peace-loving and use their skills only to defend, never to attack.

As Jedi Master Obi-Wan Kenobi's Padawan learner or apprentice, Anakin came to view Obi-Wan as the closest thing he had to a father figure.

The Force
The energy known as the Force is everywhere. Jedi learn to use the light side of the Force for good, while their enemies, the Sith, use the dark side for greed and power.

Increasing Frustration

Anakin loved and respected Obi-Wan, but often felt frustrated by him. Anakin was confident in his Jedi abilities, and felt that Obi-Wan was holding him back. He was tired of being just a Padawan.

Obi-Wan knew that Anakin had the potential to be a powerful Jedi Knight.

But he also believed that Anakin had not yet mastered his emotions, as a Jedi should. Obi-Wan was proved right when Anakin was reunited with Padmé Amidala after ten years. The feelings that Anakin had felt for her as a boy had not gone away. Soon he would no longer be able to control them.

Powerful Friend

The galaxy was formed as a Republic, which meant that it was ruled by a Senate in which all the planets had representatives. As his frustration grew, Anakin found himself turning to Chancellor Palpatine, leader of the Republic. Palpatine seemed to understand exactly how Anakin felt. He was a good listener. Anakin believed that Palpatine was on his side, unlike Obi-Wan.

Sith Lord
Palpatine was secretly a Sith Lord, Darth Sidious. He served as Supreme Chancellor of the Republic—but he had plans to destroy it.

Anakin did not realize that Palpatine was secretly trying to destroy the Republic and seize power for himself.

Unstoppable Feelings

Palpatine's sinister influence increased Anakin's frustration with Obi-Wan and the Jedi Order and left him feeling very confused. When he was chosen to escort Padmé back to Naboo, he finally lost the battle to control his feelings for her.

Padmé was now a Senator and had a duty to the Republic, but she too could not prevent herself from falling in love with Anakin. They were secretly married on Naboo. Jedi were not supposed to get emotionally attached to others. Anakin had broken the rules, but he didn't care.

Turning to the Dark Side

Anakin had not forgotten his mother Shmi, whom he had left on Tatooine. He began to have terrible nightmares about her, so he went to find her.

Out of Control
As he knelt by Shmi's grave, Anakin was angry that he could not save her. He had ignored the Jedi teachings and given into his anger.

Anakin went back to Tatooine. There he discovered that Shmi had married a farmer named Cliegg Lars, who had freed her from slavery. Anakin also learned that his mother had been kidnapped by Sand People. He went in search of her but he was too late and she died in his arms. Overcome with grief and anger, Anakin took revenge on the Sand People.

Jedi Hero

Although he was increasingly ruled by his emotions, Anakin had not yet fully turned to the dark side. When the Republic was forced into the Clone Wars, Anakin fought bravely with the Jedi.

The Clone Wars lasted for many years and Anakin and Obi-Wan became famous heroes. Anakin felt truly alive in the heat of the battle and his powers became even stronger.

However, Anakin still felt that he was being held back by the Jedi and that only Palpatine was encouraging his talents. Anakin felt that maybe the Jedi teachings were not right and that greater power lay elsewhere.

The Shadow of Death
Padmé became pregnant and Anakin began to have nightmares about her death. He had been unable to save his mother, so he was determined to save Padmé.

The Dark Side Wins

Towards the end of the Clone Wars,
Palpatine was kidnapped. Anakin and
Obi-Wan went to his aid, but it was
a trap. Sith Lord Count Dooku was
waiting for them. He knocked out
Obi-Wan and began to fight Anakin.
Palpatine urged Anakin to kill Dooku
and Anakin gave in.

A short time later Anakin chose Palpatine over the Jedi and his transition to the dark side was complete. He knelt before Palpatine—his new Sith Master.

On Palpatine's orders, Anakin led an attack on the Jedi Temple.

The End of Anakin

Anakin turned his back on the Jedi and adopted the Sith name Darth Vader. On Palpatine's orders he set out to destroy his former friends and comrades. Darth Vader also became convinced that Padmé and Obi-Wan were plotting against him. He nearly killed his wife and then faced Obi-Wan in an intense lightsaber battle.

Although Darth Vader was driven by anger and the power of the dark side, Obi-Wan won the terrible fight. Vader suffered horrific injuries and burns.

Anakin the Sith
When he turned to the dark side, Anakin's eyes turned yellow like all the Sith. He could no longer hide his alliance with evil.

Rebuilding Darth Vader

Although Darth Vader's body seemed beyond repair, Palpatine refused to give up on his evil apprentice. He took Vader's body to a secret medical facility where it was rebuilt using cyber-technology. Vader needed special breathing equipment and life support systems just to stay alive.

Behind the black armor and a black helmet, it seemed that no part of the human Anakin Skywalker was left. Darth Vader had given himself completely to the ways of the dark side.

Palpatine and his clone troopers recovered Darth Vader's broken body from the volcano planet Mustafar.

Padmé's Secret

With her husband lost to the dark side, a heartbroken Padmé gave birth to twins, whom she named Luke and Leia. Loyal Jedi Master Obi-Wan Kenobi was by her side, but Padmé had no will to live without Anakin.

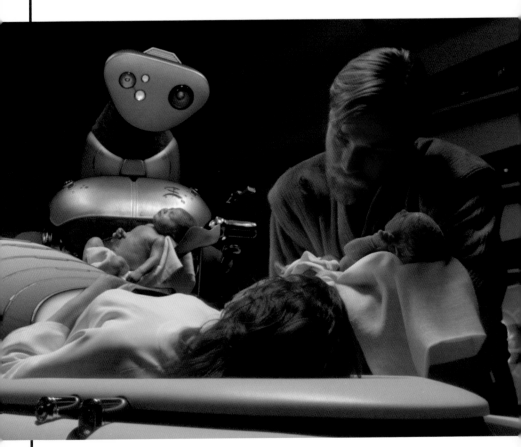

Reunited
At first Luke and Leia had no idea that they were twins, but they felt a special connection. When they discovered the truth, they were happy and not completely surprised.

Jedi Master Yoda decided to keep the children a secret from their father. Obi-Wan took Luke to Tatooine to live with Shmi Skywalker's stepson Owen Lars and his wife Beru. Luke's life on the desert planet was hard and lonely. Leia, was taken to the planet Alderaan. She was adopted by Obi-Wan's friend Bail Organa and brought up a princess. Neither twin knew that the other existed. They did not suspect that their father was the feared Sith Lord Vader.

The Rise of Darth Vader

The Republic had been destroyed and the evil Palpatine ruled the galaxy as Emperor, with Vader by his side. The Sith Lords would let nothing and no one stand in their way. Darth Vader's terrifying appearance, deep voice, and loud artificial breathing struck fear into the hearts of his enemies and allies alike. Even his own generals could not escape Vader's wrath and, as time went by, the Sith's powers grew even stronger.

Anakin Skywalker had been a brave pilot and highly skilled with a lightsaber, but the dark side of the Force continued to corrupt the mind of Darth Vader. He would strangle people without even touching them and he could read the thoughts and feelings of others.

Civil War

Although the Sith had destroyed the Republic and most of the Jedi, a small group of Rebels bravely opposed the Empire. Known as the Rebel Alliance, they were based on the planet Yavin 4. Little did Darth Vader know that two of the Rebels were his children, Luke and Leia.

The famous Jedi Master Obi-Wan Kenobi faced his former apprentice once again. This time Obi-Wan let Darth Vader win in order to show Luke that, thanks to the Force, a person's spirit continues after death.

Torture
When Darth Vader captured the Rebel Princess Leia, he tortured her to learn the Rebels' secrets. He had no idea that she was his own daughter.

Rebel Victory

The Emperor decided to build a
superweapon known as a Death Star.
It was the size of a small moon and had
the power to blow up entire planets.
However, the Rebels managed to obtain
the plans for the weapon and learned
that it had a fatal flaw.

One exhaust port was unprotected and if a pilot fired torpedoes into its shaft, a chain reaction of explosions would destroy the whole Death Star. The Rebels sent a squadron of star fighters and their best pilot, Luke Skywalker, had one chance to destroy the Death Star. He did not miss.

Imperial Fleet

The Rebel Alliance had only a small number of ships which already bore the scars of previous battles, but the Empire had a massive fleet of starships. The largest and most powerful Imperial vessels were known as Super Star Destroyers. Powered by thirteen engines, the Super Star Destroyers were arrow shaped and loaded with deadly weapons.

Darth Vader's ship *Executor* was the most powerful Super Star Destroyer. Vader commanded the fleet, but the Emperor gave his orders via hologram.

Executor
Vader's magnificent ship led the Imperial fleet into many great battles. It was eventually destroyed by the Rebels.

Vader's Revenge

When the Rebels blew up the first Death Star, it made Darth Vader and the Emperor extremely angry. They began building a new Death Star and Darth Vader set out to find and destroy the Rebels responsible. Vader sent probe droids to every corner of the galaxy to find the Rebels' new base. He finally located them on the ice planet Hoth.

Although Darth Vader won the Battle of Hoth, he was not able to destroy the Rebels' best ship, the Millenium Falcon.

The Sith Lord traveled to Hoth with the Imperial fleet and launched a deadly attack. The Rebels had to evacuate very quickly and their forces were scattered far and wide across the galaxy.

Luke Skywalker

After having a vision in which his friends were in danger, Luke Skywalker flew to Cloud City, near the gas planet Bespin. He was now more powerful thanks to the teachings of Jedi Master Yoda.

Cloud City

Emperor Palpatine had finally told Darth Vader the truth about Luke Skywalker. As Darth Vader laid a trap for Luke on Cloud City, he was looking for more than just a troublesome Rebel— he was searching for his son.

As Luke and Vader fought with lightsabers, Luke still had no idea who lay behind Darth Vader's mask. The fight ended when Vader chopped off Luke's hand. He revealed that he was Luke's father and asked his son to join him and rule the galaxy. Despite his painful wound, Luke was strong with the Force. He refused to turn to the dark side.

Vader's Choice

For many years, Darth Vader had been loyal to Emperor Palpatine. However, meeting his son Luke—a good and true person—seemed to change him. Could it be that some part of Anakin Skywalker remained behind Vader's mask?

Palpatine had predicted that Luke would come to them and he would be turned to the dark side. When Luke surrendered, it seemed that Palpatine would be proved right. As father and son fought once more, Luke felt anger and hatred and drew close to the dark side. At the last moment Luke was able to control his feelings and refused to join the dark side. As an enraged Palpatine attacked Luke, Anakin Skywalker finally returned from the dark side to save his son.

Death of an Emperor
As Palpatine tortured Luke with deadly Force lightning, Darth Vader could not bear to watch. He picked up his Master and threw him down a bottomless reactor shaft. The Emperor was dead!

The Death of Darth Vader

At the vital moment, Darth Vader returned from his nightmare. Luke had reminded him that he was once a great Jedi named Anakin Skywalker. However, as Vader saved his son, he was fatally wounded by the Emperor.

As Anakin lay dying, he asked Luke to remove his helmet so that he could look at his son's face with his own eyes. When Anakin died, his body disappeared into the light side of the Force. Luke was sad that his father was dead but proud of him too. The light side of the Force had overcome the dark side and Anakin Skywalker had returned.

On the forest moon of Endor, Luke burned Vader's armor. All around the galaxy, everyone celebrated the end of Palpatine and his evil Empire.

Jedi Restored
After his death, Anakin took his place with the other great Jedi heroes Yoda and Obi-Wan Kenobi.

Glossary

Apprentice
A person who is learning a skill.

Dark side
The part of the Force associated with fear and hatred.

Droid
A kind of robot.

Emperor
The leader of an Empire is called an Emperor. Palpatine is the Emperor who rules the Galactic Empire.

Empire
A group of nations ruled over by one leader, who is called an Emperor.

The Force
An energy field created by all living things.

Force lightning
One of the Sith's powers which involves firing deadly electricity from their fingers.

Galaxy
A group of millions of stars and planets.

Jedi Council
The governing body of the Jedi order. The wisest Jedi, such as Yoda, sit on the Council.

Jedi Knight
A *Star Wars* warrior with special powers who defends the good of the galaxy. Anakin Skywalker, Luke Skywalker, and Ob-Wan Kenobi are all Jedi Knights.

Jedi Master
The most experienced Jedi of all.

Jedi Order
The name of a group that defends peace and justice in the galaxy.

Jedi Temple
The Jedi headquarters where the Jedi Council meets and Jedi live, train, and work.

Lightsaber
A Jedi's and Sith's weapon, made of glowing energy.

Light side
The part of the Force associated with goodness, compassion, and healing.

Missions
Special tasks or duties.

Padawan Learner
A Jedi who is learning the ways of the Force.

Rebel
Someone who opposes whoever is in power.

Republic
A nation or group of nations in which the people vote for their leaders.

Senate
The governing body of the Republic.

Senator
A member of the Senate. He or she will have been chosen (elected) by the people of his or her country.

Sith
Enemies of the Jedi who use the dark side of the Force.

Slave
A person who is owned by another person.

Starfighter
A small, fast spaceship used by Jedi and others.

Index